MY TIME OF YEAR

by katharine dow

pictures by walter erhard

New York
Henry Z. Walck Incorporated
1961

To Willie, Katy and Jimmy

In summer I sit in the sun.

Where I live

the summer sun shines hot,

so hot the sand burns our feet

and we hop to the cool water.

In summer

the heat makes everything still...
except for the hum of the lawnmower

and the tinkle of ice

in lemonade glasses,

as we sip in the shade.

Where I live the summer sun
melts the tar in the street,

and it sticks to our shoes.

The sprinkler cools us
and the brown grass, too.

In summer the weather is hot
and we wear shorts.

But where I live fall comes

with a breeze and a sweater

...and school.

The sky is bright blue

and the leaves turn
red and orange and yellow,
and crisp.

In fall we run hard and skip.

We rake leaves and burn them
and carve pumpkins and eat apples.

But where I live fall doesn't stay.

Winter comes,

with the first snow

and mittens,

and scarves tied around our heads.

The wind feels icy
against our cheeks.

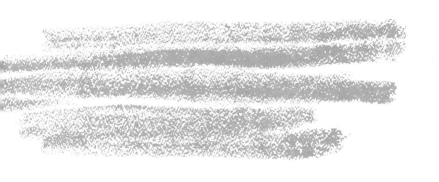

In winter we move fast
on sleds and skates.

And indoors is nice in winter,

by the fire, drinking hot chocolate

and listening to the wind...outside.

But where I live

the snow begins to melt

and the wind blows warm again.

Spring comes.

We take off our jackets
to skip rope or play marbles.

The spring sun is warm
and the spring rain is soft.

The flowers grow yellow and pink

and the grass turns green.

School ends and spring ends, too.

Summer is here.

Where I live the seasons come

one   after   the   other.

And the season it is, is the one I like.